Five-Minute Fillers

Foundation–Y2

**Fun and confidence-boosting
activities to help children
memorise number facts**

Contents

Times-tables

SECTION 2: ACTIVITIES WHILST WAITING FOR CHILDREN TO FINISH CHANGING 34

Counting

Addition

Number bonds

Subtraction

More or less

Doubling and halving

Times-tables

SECTION 3: ACTIVITIES FOR THOSE SPARE 5 MINUTES 53

Five-Minute Fillers

Learn by heart and practise basic skills – a no tears, no time approach

These are short rehearsal activities which teachers can use whilst standing in a queue outside the hall, waiting to go in to assembly, before dismissing children, when there are 5 minutes before lunch or play and during the time children are changing back into their uniforms after PE. The activities are categorised under these different contexts as well as by topic. They all indicate the approximate ages of children for whom they would be appropriate and are presented in order of age including Foundation (F), Year 1 (Y1) and Year 2 (Y2). Each activity is intended to be done in a short time with the whole class or a large group.

Five-Minute Fillers are activities that:
- can be completed in 5 minutes or less
- require no resources
- are oral rather than written
- are suitable for the whole class or a large group
- children will improve at with familiarity
- will build children's confidence.

This last point is key. Children are miserably aware if they are struggling to remember things which other children visibly have at their finger-tips. None of this mathematics is rocket science. All of it is accessible and easily doable by 99.9% of children. It simply requires that children are able to memorise facts and to practise particular basic skills until these become automatic and no longer require conscious effort. As children engage repeatedly in these activities, they can hone their skills and improve their performance. Children like repetition; it engenders confidence and they enjoy the knowledge that they are getting good at something. The crucial and easy-to-satisfy criteria for success are 'little and often' and 'learning by heart' – nothing that cannot be achieved in any classroom in any school!

Rationale

Children do not routinely memorise things as they used to. Whereas I entered school already having learned by heart several dozen nursery rhymes poems and prayers, children nowadays are no longer encouraged or required to memorise in this way. Technology has, in this respect, usurped memory. We see this very clearly with older students.

When I ask my GCSE maths class for their mobile numbers, they reach in their pockets to find their phones. Only a few have bothered to memorise their phone numbers. Contrasting this with my own experience, at 16 I knew at least 20, possibly 30 or more, phone numbers by heart which enabled me to race home and call my friends before my parents arrived back from work. I had memorised the words of all my favourite pop songs and in addition I possessed within my own head, although I did not then realise or appreciate it, a wealth of literature in the form of poems, sayings, texts and passages, all of which I had, however reluctantly, memorised at the behest of my elders and betters.

So how does all of this affect mathematics and its teaching? Like every other subject, mathematics relies to a certain degree upon memory. To a greater extent than some, it helps if basic facts and skills are internalised so thoroughly that, by the time children need to master more complex algorithms and procedures, these are on what we may term 'automatic pilot'. Knowing number bonds up to 20, knowing how to add multiples of ten, knowing 1 or 10 more or less than a given number, counting on or back in 1s, counting in 2s, 5s and 10s, knowing the x2, x3, x5 and x10 tables, as well as prerequisite skills such as being able to say the 'next' number and chanting the numbers in order to 100 and beyond are all skills which children require on automatic pilot by the time they enter the junior years. Only if these facts are thoroughly memorised can we be sure that children will be able to draw upon these basic building blocks as they develop the more complicated mental calculation strategies and the less intuitive written calculation methods required.

The memory, like any other part of the person, atrophies and becomes useless if it is not exercised. It therefore becomes essential to include memorisation as a more major part of the school curriculum. The absence of basic mathematical facts and skills acts to disadvantage children from the age of 7 onwards. It is therefore essential that we, as teachers, become more proactive in encouraging memorisation of these facts and skills.

It will be objected that there is simply not enough time in the day for all of the things we currently have to do as infant teachers. This is true. However, it is also the case that the key to effective memorisation is 'little and often' rather than learning in large chunks and infrequently. All of these Five-Minute Fillers are intended to enable teachers to use those 'wasted' moments of the school day. Such times can be utilised to help children not only to learn by heart all of the above-mentioned skills, but also to have fun and enjoy learning them.

Section I: Activities whilst lining up

Advice to teachers

- Keep the pace brisk – the activities rely on a brisk pace and a no-nonsense approach.
- Send children to the back of the line – many activities require that those who do not respond quickly enough, or with the correct answer, are sent to the back of the line. Do not worry about this. Make it clear that this is not a punishment; it is part of the fun. If this is done swiftly and with no fuss it will just be treated as a move in the game. You will be surprised by how quickly children start to remember things!
- Position yourself halfway down the line, or even towards the back. This helps everyone, not just those at the front, to feel involved.
- Keep the activities good-humoured and light-hearted. Do not attempt to tell children off or reprove them. These activities are intended to be fun, not work!
- The key to successful activities is generating a 'can do' atmosphere and giving children a lot of confidence and praise. Keep stressing how good children are getting at knowing their number facts. Keep telling them that they are all really improving at maths now and that they will be brilliant mathematicians when they reach the juniors!

Counting

FMFI.I   Silent counting

(F) Counting to 20 and beyond

Line children up. Tell children to watch your mouth carefully. Ask the first child in the line to say *One*. You silently mouth *Two*. Point to the second child, who says *Three*. If the child does not know what number to say they go to the back of the line. Continue, silently mouthing *Four*. Point to the next child, who says *Five*, then the next child, who says *Six*. You mouth *Seven*. Point to the next child to say *Eight* and the next child to say *Nine*. You mouth *Ten*. Keep pointing, sometimes to just one child, sometimes to two or three children in a row, then mouthing the next number. Can children keep count?

Adaptations

Can also be used for:

* counting backwards to 0   (F)

Counting

FMF1.2   Finger match

(F) Matching a number to a quantity

Line children up and choose a child. Say a 1-digit number. The child promptly shows you that number of fingers. If they are correct, they stay where they are. If not, they quickly go to the back of the line. Choose another child and say a number. They also show you that number of fingers. Keep playing at a fast pace so that there is always one child showing fingers and another either staying where they are in the line or moving to the back.

Adaptations

Can also be used for:

- holding up the number of fingers that is 1 more than the number said   (F / Y1)
- holding up the number of fingers that is 1 less than the number said   (F / Y1)

Counting

FMF1.3   Tapping Count

(F) Counting to 100

Line children up. Say any starting number, for example *Twenty*. Choose a child in the line. Lightly tap them on the shoulders. As you tap, they say the next number in the count. Tap the shoulders of another child in the line. They say the following number. Keep tapping children lightly on the shoulders to continue the count. Repeat with a different starting number.

Adaptations

Can also be used for:

- counting backwards   (F / Y1)
- counting in 2s, either from 1 or from 2   (Y1 / Y2)
- counting in steps of different sizes, for example 3s, 5s or 10s (Y2+)

Counting

FMFI.4   Letters in my name

(F) Counting to 10, knowing numbers without counting

Line children up. Point to the first child in the line. They say the number of letters in their name. If they do this quickly and correctly, they stay where they are in the line. If they are slow or give an incorrect answer, they go to the back of the line. The first child then points to another child who says the number of letters in their name. Once again, if they are slow or give the incorrect total, then they go to the back of the line. Work down the line, keeping a fast pace, instructing children to point to one another and say the number of letters in their names.

Adaptations

Can also be used for:

- saying the number of fingers held up and shown   (F)

Counting

FMF1.5   Hands on shoulders

(F / Y1) Counting in 10s

Line children up. *We will count in tens down the line and see how far we can get. I hope we can count all the way into the hundreds!* Start with the first child in the line who turns to face the second child, puts both hands (ten fingers) on their shoulders and says *Ten*. Then the second child turns to face the third child, puts both hands on their shoulders and says *Twenty*. Children keep turning, placing ten fingers on one another's shoulders, and saying the number that is 10 more. Keep going past 100 and even 200, helping children to cross the hundreds.

Adaptations

Can also be used for:

- saying the number 1 more, putting one hand on one shoulder each time   (F)
- saying the number 1 less   (F)
- saying the number 10 less, starting at 100 and repeating   (F / Y1)

Counting

FMFI.6   Off the bus

(F / YI) Counting back in Is

Line children up. *Imagine you are all on my bus.* Say the number of people on the bus (the total number of children in class that day). For example, *There are twenty-six people on my bus today.* Point to a child and say *Time for you to get off the bus!* That child does a little jump, as if getting off the bus, and says the number I less than the total, for example *Twenty-five.* You say *There are now twenty-five people on my bus!* Point to another child, who also does a little jump and says the number I less than that, *Twenty-four.* Keep going until there is no one left on the bus.

Adaptations

Can also be used for:

- counting back in 2s, if you choose two children at a time   (YI / Y2)

Counting

FMFI.7   Charge along

(YI) Counting in I0s from any given number

Line children up. Face the first child in the line. Say a number between 0 and I0 and mime handing the number to the child. They take it in their hand, add I0 to it, say the new total and mime handing it to the next child in the line. Children keep passing the imaginary number down the line, adding I0 each time. If a child cannot quickly say the new total, they go to the back of the line.

Adaptations

Can also be used for:

- saying the number I more or I less   (F)
- saying the number 5 more   (YI / Y2)

Counting

FMFI.8   Hop along halves

(Y2+) Counting in $\frac{1}{2}$s

Line children up. Choose a child in the line and tell them that you are starting a count, counting up in $\frac{1}{2}$s. *One half.* They respond by saying the next number, *One,* then quickly choose another child and clap their hands at them. The second child says the next number in the halves count, *One and a half.* They choose a child to say the next number, clap at them and so on. Keep a brisk pace, and a clear rhythm; *Half, clap, One, clap, One and a half, clap, Two, clap, Two and a half, clap* ... and so on.

Adaptations

Can also be used for:

* counting in $\frac{1}{4}$s   (Y2+)

Addition

FMF1.9   Instant sums

(Y1) Adding pairs of numbers below 10

Line children up. *We are going to do some really fast calculations!* Choose a child. Say any number and simultaneously hold up a different number of fingers. The child quickly adds the two numbers and says the total. If they are slow or incorrect, they kneel down. Choose another child and repeat. Keep a fast pace. Sometimes choose children who are kneeling down so that they get a second chance. Try to go fast enough for every child to have at least one go.

Adaptations

Can also be used for:

- saying the number 10 more or 10 less   (Y1 / Y2)

Addition

FMFI.10   Total up

(YI / Y2+) Adding I-digit numbers

Line children up. *We are going to do a huge calculation!* Say *One* and point to the first child in the line. They choose whether to add 2 or 3, then turn to the second child and say the answer. For example, they add 2 and say *Three.* The second child then decides whether to add 2 or 3, turns to the third child and says the answer, for example *Six.* Continue like this, making sure children respond quickly to keep a fast pace.

Adaptations

Can also be used for:

- subtracting 2 or 3 from a starting number above 60   (YI / Y2)
- adding a multiple of ten   (Y2+)

Addition

FMF1.11   Keep it going!

(Y2+) Recognising units patterns in addition

Line children up. *We are going to say additions in turn. Each addition should use the same ones digits as the addition before.* Position yourself at the back of the line. Start by saying *8 + 5 = 13* to the child at the back of the line. They say another addition which uses the same 1s digits, for example *38 + 5 = 43*. Then they gently tap the child in front of them who says another addition using the same 1s digits, for example *78 + 5 = 83*. Keep going as far up the line as you can, with each child saying an addition that has not been said before. Encourage children to realise that they could say 25 + 8 = 33 as well as 28 + 5 = 33 and try to keep going for the whole length of the line. If any child is incorrect or too slow they go to the back of the line, behind you.

Adaptations

Can also be used for:

- looking at subtraction patterns, for example 34 – 5, 14 – 5 etc. (Y2+)

Number bonds

FMF1.12   Jumping to 10

(Y1) Number bonds to 10 and other number bonds

Line children up. Say a number less than 10 and point to the first child. They respond by jumping on the spot the number of times to match with your number to make 10. For example, you say *Six* and they jump four times. If the child does the wrong number of jumps they go to the back of the line. Move down the line, say another number less than 10 and point to the second child. They respond by clapping the number of times to match with your number to make 10. Repeat, alternating jumping and clapping, keeping a fast pace.

Adaptations

Can also be used for:

- jumping the number needed to make 5, 6, 7, 8 or 9   (F / Y1)

Number bonds

FMF1.13   Speak out!

(Y1 / Y2) Bonds to 10 and other number bonds

Line children up. Say a number less than 10 and point to the first child in the line. They respond by quickly saying the number which adds to your number to make 10. For example, you say *Four* and they say *Six*. If they are incorrect or slow to answer, they go to the back of the line. Work down the line at a fast pace, saying numbers and letting children respond.

Adaptations

Can also be used for:

- saying pairs of numbers that make 6, 7, 8 or 9   (F / Y1)
- saying pairs of numbers that make 20   (Y2+)
- saying pairs of numbers that make all the numbers up to 20 (Y2+)

Number bonds

FMF1.14   Bond with me

(Y1 / Y2+) Number bonds for numbers up to 20

Line children up. Point to the first child in the line and ask them to turn to the child behind them and say a number between 10 and 20, for example *Thirteen*. The next child responds with an addition that has the first number as a total, for example *Six plus seven*. If correct, the second child turns to the child behind them and says the original number again, *Thirteen*. The third child responds with a different addition that has the same total, for example *Eight and five*. If they are correct, the third child turns to the next child. Continue with two or three more children. Children who do not respond promptly or correctly go to the back of the line. When the total has been made in several ways, ask a child to say a new number, for example *Fifteen*, and continue. Keep a fast pace.

Adaptations

Can also be used for:

- saying pairs of numbers that make 6, 7, 8 or 9   (F / Y1)
- saying the number bonds to 10   (Y1 / Y2)
- saying pairs of numbers that make 20   (Y2+)
- saying pairs of numbers that make 100   (Y2+)

Number bonds

FMFI.I5 Whispers to I5

(Y2+) Pairs of numbers that make the numbers up to 20

Line children up. Ask the child at the front of the line to whisper a number between 3 and I5 to the second child, for example *Seven*. The second child says aloud the number to add to the whispered number to make I5, *Eight*. Confirm with the first child that this is the correct answer. If it is, ask the second child to whisper a number between 3 and I5 to the third child. If it is not, ask the second child to go to the back of the line. Continue until most of the bonds to I5 have been said, then start again with a new total, for example *Eighteen*. Keep a fast pace. Try to go fast enough for every child to have at least one go.

Adaptations

Can also be used for:

- practising the number bonds for numbers up to 6 (F)
- practising the number bonds for numbers up to I0 (YI)

Subtraction

FMF1.16 Fold down fingers

(Y1) Subtracting from numbers up to 10

Line children up. Choose a child. Ask them to show you a
number of fingers using both hands, for example seven fingers.
Fold down two! The child folds down two fingers. They say
the number that is left. Reiterate by saying the subtraction,
Seven take away two is five. Then move on to the next child.
Ask children to subtract 2, sometimes 3 or even 4. Keep a fast
pace, with quick-fire subtractions. If a child responds slowly or
incorrectly, they go to the back of the line.

Adaptations

Can also be used for:

- saying the number 1 less   (F / Y1)
- subtracting a multiple of ten (give a 2-digit number and ask
  children to subtract the number of tens shown by their fingers)
  (Y1 / Y2)

Subtraction

FMFI.I7   Twenty finger take-aways

(YI / Y2+) Subtracting from 20

Line children up in pairs. Point to the first pair. *Show me twenty fingers.* The children in the pair hold up their four hands, with all twenty fingers showing. Say a number less than 10 to one of the children in the pair, for example *Eight.* The child folds down eight fingers and the pair quickly agree the number that is left and say it. Reiterate by saying the subtraction, *Twenty take away eight is twelve.* If the children do this quickly and correctly, they stay standing up. If they are slow or incorrect, both children kneel down. Point to the next pair and ask them to hold up twenty fingers. Say a number less than 20, for example *Sixteen.* Between them the pair fold down sixteen fingers and say the number that is left. Reiterate by saying the subtraction, *Twenty take away sixteen is four.* Keep going down the line, maintaining a fast pace. Try to go fast enough for kneeling pairs to get a second chance.

Adaptations

Can also be used for:

- subtracting from 10 using one hand from each child to make ten fingers between them   (YI)

More or less

FMF1.18 'Next' numbers

(F / Y1) Saying the next number without counting from 1

Line children up. Say a number then point to any child. They respond promptly, saying the next number in the count (children may not start counting from 1 to find the answer). For example if you say *Nine*, they quickly say *Ten*. If they are correct, they go to the front of the line. If they are incorrect, they go to the back of the line. Keep a fast pace so that children are constantly moving or waiting for their turn.

Adaptations

Can also be used for:

- saying the number 1 less   (F / Y1)
- saying the number 10 more   (Y1 / Y2)
- saying the number 10 less   (Y2+)
- saying the number 100 more or less   (Y2+)

More or less

FMF1.19   More or less

(F / Y1) Saying a number 1 more or less than a given number

Line children up. Hold your hand up, with the palm facing the first child in the line. That child holds up their own hand in the same way and you say any number, for example *Sixteen*. They respond with the number 1 more, *Seventeen*, and clap their hand against your hand. If they are quick and correct, they turn to the next child. This time they hold their hand out palm upwards. The first child says any number, for example *Nine*. The second child claps their hand down on the first child's hand and says the number 1 less, *Eight*. If they are quick and correct, they turn to the third child in the line. They hold their hand up, with the palm facing the third child. The second child says a number to the third child, who responds by saying the number 1 more and clapping hands. Keep going like this, with children doing 'high five' claps when saying the number 1 more, and 'low five' claps when saying the number 1 less. If a child does not give a quick or correct answer, they go to the back of the line.

Adaptations

Can also be used for:

- saying the number 10 more or 10 less   (Y1 / Y2)
- saying the number 2 more or 2 less   (Y2+)

Doubling and halving

FMFI.20   Double or quit

(Y2+) Doubling numbers to 20 and beyond

Line children up. Say a I-digit number to the child at the front of the line. They double it and say the answer to the child behind them. The second child doubles that number and says the answer to the child behind them. The third child doubles that number, and so on. When the number gets too large for children to double, start again with a new I-digit number. Keep a fast pace and see how many times a number can be doubled before it gets too big.

Adaptations

Can also be used for:

- halving numbers where no ten has to be crossed (for example 48, 80, 68, 100)   (YI / Y2)

Doubling and halving

FMF1.21   Half your size

(Y2+) Halving odd and even numbers

Line children up. Point to a child in the line and say any number. The child responds by saying half of that number. For example, you say *Seventeen*, the child says *Eight and a half*. Point to another child and choose whether to ask them to halve an odd number or an even number. If it is an odd number, the child gives their answer as a mixed number, for example *Four and a half*. If a child cannot respond promptly or correctly, they kneel down in the line. Continue, keeping a fast pace. Try to go fast enough for kneeling children to get a second chance.

Adaptations

Can also be used for:

- practising finding quarters of multiples of 4   (Y2+)
- practising halving even numbers to 100 (not crossing tens)   (Y2+)

Doubling and halving

FMF1.22   Chains

(Y2+) Halving and adding 1

Line children up. *We are going to create a chain of numbers. We
will pass a number down the line. When you receive the number
think about whether it is odd or even. If it is even, halve it before
you pass it on. If it is odd, add one before you pass it on.* Start
the chain by saying *Eighteen* to the first child. They halve it and
say *Nine* to the second child. That child should add 1 and say *Ten*
to the third child. They halve it and say *Five* to the fourth child.
That child adds 1 and says *Six* to the fifth child, and so on. When
the chain ends by reaching 1, start a new chain. What is the
longest chain we can make?

Adaptations

Can also be used for:

- subtracting 2 or 3 from a starting number above 60   (Y1 / Y2)
- adding a multiple of ten   (Y2+)

Times-tables

FMFI.23   Two times-table all wrong!

(Y2) Know the two times-table

Chant the two times-table like this: *One two is zoo*. Then tap the first child to say the correct answer, *Two*. *Two twos are door*, tap a child to say the correct *Four*. *Three twos are fix*, tap a child to say *Six*. Continue like this, tapping a different child each time. If they cannot say the correct answer immediately, they go to the back of the line. *Four twos are gate... Five twos are hen... Six twos are delve... Seven twos are sorting... Eight twos are all clean... Nine twos are waiting... Ten twos are plenty...!*

Adaptations

Can also be used for:

- five times-table: *One five is alive, Two fives are hen, Three fives are super keen, Four fives are plenty, Five fives are bees in a hive, Six fives are dirty, Seven fives are dirt alive, Eight fives are naughty, Nine fives are naught-alive, Ten fives are nifty!*   (Y2)
- ten times-table: *One ten is Ben, Two tens are plenty, Three tens are dirty, Four tens are naughty, Five tens are nifty, Six tens are pixie, Seven tens are heavenly, Eight tens are weighty, Nine tens are fine-tea, Ten tens are bumbly...!*   (Y2)

Times-tables

FMFI.24   Clapping tables

(Y2) Know the two times-table

Ask children to hold up their hands, palms facing outwards.
Choose a child and clap their hands with both of yours a number
of times, counting as you do so. For example, *One, two, three* as
you clap three times. They have to say the number that many 2s
make, for example *Six*. If they are too slow, they go to the back
of the line. Choose another child and clap both of their hands
with both of yours, *One, two, three, four, five, six*. That child must
say *Twelve* really quickly or they also go to the back of the line.
This activity requires a bit of practice. Keep the pace fast and
encourage children to count in 2s as you clap their hands, so that
they will have the answer ready when it is their turn!

Adaptations

Can also be used for:

- five times-table   (Y2)
- ten times-table   (Y2)

Section 2: Activities whilst waiting for children to finish changing

Advice to teachers

- Keep the pace brisk – the activities rely on a brisk pace and a no-nonsense approach.
- Children join in with the activity as they finish getting changed. The activities should be seen to be fun so that children will want to join in!
- Start the activities once five or six children have finished dressing.
- If at all possible, have a small reward for all those who participate.
- Children will be constantly joining the activity as they finish changing, so make room to include them as they arrive.
- Keep the activities really active as well as fast-moving. Do not attempt to tell children off or reprove them. These activities are intended to be fun, not work!
- The key to successful activities is generating a 'can do' atmosphere and giving children a lot of confidence and praise. Keep stressing how good children are getting at knowing their number facts. Keep telling them that they are all really improving at maths now and that they will be brilliant mathematicians when they reach the juniors!

Counting

FMF2.I   Sing-a-long numbers

(F) Matching a number to fingers

When the first five or six children are dressed, sit them in a circle. Include other children in the circle as they finish getting ready. Together sing *A ship came from China* (Appendix I). At the end of the third line, say a I-digit number and hold up the matching number of fingers, for example *It brought me a six*. During the last line, children in the circle show the matching number of fingers and shake them in time to the music. Repeat, this time asking the child on your left to sing a number and show the matching number of fingers. Continue, each time letting the next child in the circle sing a number before the rest of the group show the matching number of fingers.

Adaptations

Can also be used for:

- saying the name of a shape – children all draw this in the air at *like this, like this*   (F)

Counting

FMF2.2 Pass an addition along

(Y1) Adding 3 or 4 to a given number

When the first five or six children are dressed, sit them in a circle. Include other children in the circle as they finish getting ready. Say an addition, for example *Five plus three*, and mime carefully handing it to the child sitting next to you, as if it is very delicate and precious. They say the answer to the addition, *Eight*. If they are correct, they say the addition that is their total plus 3, *Eight plus three*, and mime carefully passing it to the next child. Continue, adding 3 each time. If a child gives an incorrect answer then the addition 'breaks'. If this happens then start again with a new addition, for example *Seven plus four*. This time children add 4 each time. How long can children continue before the addition 'breaks'?

Adaptations

Can also be used for:

- subtraction – counting back 1, 2 or 3 (Y1)
- adding or subtracting 10 (Y2)

Counting

FMF2.3   Boy, girl, boy, girl

(YI / Y2) Counting in I0s

When children are ready, they join you on the floor. When there are five or six children, say a number, for example *Thirty-seven*, and point to a boy. He comes and kneels in front of you and says the number that is 10 more, *Forty-seven*. Then say a new number, for example *Forty-three*, and point to a girl. She comes and kneels in front of you, next to the boy, and says the number 10 less, *Thirty-three*. Repeat, alternating boys and girls, 10 more and 10 less, until you have created a line of boys and a line of girls. Any children who do not answer promptly or correctly do not join a line. When you have two lines of more than ten children, count back in 10s from a number down the girls' line and count on in 10s from a number up the boys' line.

Adaptations

Can also be used for:

- counting in Is   (F)
- counting in 5s   (YI / Y2)

Counting

FMF2.4   Number in my pocket

(YI / Y2) Number properties

When children are ready, they join you on the floor. When there are five or six children, say *I have a number in my pocket, can you guess what number it is?* Give them a range, for example *It is less than one hundred* or *It is a two-digit number.* Explain that they can take turns to ask you questions about the number, but you can only answer with *Yes* or *No.* Hold up a finger for every question asked. Discuss which questions might be helpful and which might be unhelpful. For example *Is it sixteen?* is unhelpful because it only rules out one number. Examples of helpful questions are *Is it less than fifty?*, *Is it even?* and *Is the first digit a six?* Include other children as they are ready. How many questions does it take to guess your number? Choose another number and see if children can guess it with fewer questions.

Adaptations

Can also be used for:

- numbers below 20   (YI)
- numbers above 100   (Y2+)

Addition

FMF 2.5   Pass the number

(F / YI) Adding 2 to a given number

When the first five or six children are dressed, sit them in a circle. Include other children in the circle as they finish getting ready. Say a number, for example *Seven*, and mime passing it to the child on your left. They add 2 to this number, say the answer, *Nine*, then mime passing the new number to the next child. The child receiving it has to add 2 to this number and say the result, *Eleven*. Continue in this way, with children passing the number and adding 2 each time. Include all children in the circle and keep the pace brisk.

Adaptations

Can also be used for:

- adding I to a number   (F /YI)
- adding 3 or 4 to a number   (YI)
- adding I0 to a number   (YI / Y2)

Addition

FMF2.6 Stand up, sit down!

(Y2) Using number facts to help addition

When children are ready, they join you and sit on the floor. When there are five or six children, say an addition, for example *Seven plus five*. Point to a child who promptly tells you the answer. Then say an addition with the same Is digits, for example *Twenty-seven plus five*, and point to another child. They quickly tell you the answer. Repeat eight times, ensuring that children notice the pattern. If a child responds quickly and correctly, they stand up. If not, they stay sitting. Once a child is standing, if they answer correctly then they sit down, and they continue to stand up or sit down each time they are correct. If a child answers incorrectly then they stay as they were.

Adaptations

Can also be used for:

- simple I-digit plus I-digit sums   (YI)

Addition

FMF2.7   Fast sums

(Y2) Using number facts to help addition

When children are ready, they join you and sit on the floor. When there are five or six children, explain that you are going to say some additions very quickly. For each addition, children quickly show you the Is digit of the answer using their fingers. For example you say *Sixteen plus seven* and children show you three fingers. Repeat, saying additions with the same Is digits, for example *Thirty-six plus seven*. Keep a fast pace. Do children realise that they are always showing the same number of fingers? Repeat with other Is digits and confirm that children notice the pattern.

Adaptations

Can also be used for:

* simple I-digit plus I-digit sums   (YI)

Number bonds

FMF2.8 Sit on my hands!

(F / Y1) Bonds to 10

When children are ready, they join you and sit on the floor. As each child joins you, choose a 1-digit number and silently show them that number of fingers. They quickly show you the number of fingers that match yours to make 10. If they are incorrect or answer too slowly, they sit on their hands. Continue to show a number of fingers to children as they join. Go back to children who have already had a turn, including children who are sitting on their hands, so that they get a second chance.

Adaptations

Can also be used for:

- saying pairs of numbers that make 6, 7, 8 and 9   (F)
- saying pairs of numbers that make 20   (Y2)

Number bonds

FMF2.9   Whisper along

(Y2) Bonds to 20

When the first five or six children are dressed, sit them in a circle. Include other children in the circle as they are ready. Whisper a number between 10 and 20 to the child sitting next to you. They show the number of fingers that goes with your number to make 20. For example, you whisper *Twelve*, they show eight fingers. Ask the other children to look at the fingers, think what number goes with that to make 20 and then say the number that you whispered, *Twelve*. Then the first child whispers a number between 10 and 20 to the child next to them. The second child shows the number of fingers that goes with the number to make 20. The other children say the number that was whispered. Continue, moving round the circle. If a child shows an incorrect number, then the child next to them takes over and whispers the next number.

Adaptations

Can also be used for:

- making the bonds to 10   (Y1)
- saying pairs of numbers that make the numbers between 10 and 20   (Y2+)

Number bonds

FMF2.10   Making 60

(Y2) Pairs of numbers that add to 60 (multiples of 5)

When children are ready, they join you and sit on the floor. When there are five or six children, say *We are going to make sixty. Sixty is the number of minutes in an hour.* Say a number, for example *Thirty-five*. Children use their fingers to quickly show you what goes with this number to make 60. Their left hand is the number of 10s, and their right hand is the number of 1s. For example, they show 25 with two fingers on the left hand and five fingers on the right hand. You keep saying numbers and children quickly show you the bond to 60 on their fingers. Reward children who consistently give correct answers.

Adaptations

Can also be used for:

- pairs of multiples of 5 that add to 100   (Y2+)

Subtraction

FMF2.II   Step down maths

(Y1) Subtracting from numbers less than 30

When children are ready, they join you and sit on the floor. When there are five or six children, ask one of them to stand up and come to the front. Say a number less than 30. That child says the number that is 3 less. For example, you say *Twenty-eight*, they say *Twenty-five*. If they answer quickly and correctly, they stay standing at the front. If not, they sit back down. Ask another child to stand next to the first child. They say the number that is 3 less again, *Twenty-two*. If they are correct, they kneel next to the first child. If not, they sit back down. Ask the next child to say the number that is 3 less again, *Nineteen*. If they are correct, they kneel down lower than the second child. If not, they sit back down. Keep going like this, creating a line of children at the front where each one is lower in height than the child before them; standing, kneeling, kneeling down, sitting down, crouching, lying down. Repeat with another number less than 30, this time asking children to say the number 4 less.

Adaptations

Can also be used for:

- counting back in multiples of ten   (Y2)

Subtraction

FMF2.I2   Give me my change

(YI / Y2) Giving change from 20p

When children are ready, they join you and sit on the floor.
As each child joins you, tell them a fun item and a price. They
imagine that they are the shopkeeper and quickly say the
change they would give you from 20p. For example, you say *I
want to buy a sticker at I2p*. They say *That is 8p change*. If they
do this quickly and correctly, they sit down. If not, they remain
standing. Keep a fast pace and encourage children to use bonds
to I0 to help. Continue, sometimes returning to children who are
standing so that they get a second chance.

Adaptations

Can also be used for:

- giving change from 50p or £I   (YI / Y2+)

More or less

FMF2.13   1 or 10 more or less

(Y1) Know the number 1 more or less and 10 more

Choose a child who is ready. Show a number on your fingers.
They look at your fingers and turn to the next child and say
either *More* or *Less*. The second child says a number 1 more or
less than the number you showed. So if you show five fingers and
the first child says *More*, then the second child says *Six*. If they do
this correctly, they turn to another child and show a number of
fingers. They say either *More* or *Less* and the following child has
to say the number 1 more or less as appropriate. Children keep
passing the numbers round like this until you interrupt. At any
point you can point to a child and say *Ten more!* and they have
to say the number 10 more, for example, they are showing six
fingers so they have to say *Sixteen*. Keep a fast pace.

Adaptations

Can also be used for:

- saying the number 10 more or less, as long as you do not show
  a number on your fingers but instead say a number, for example
  Thirty-five, so that the next child can say a number 10 more or 10
  less   (Y2)

More or less

FMF2.14   Thumbs up or thumbs down

(Y2) Say whether a number is more or less than another given number

Collect children on the carpet as they are ready. As each child comes to the carpet, ask them to say a 2-digit number. Start with the first child, for example they say *Fifty-six*. When the next child arrives, they should say another 2-digit number, for example *Forty-nine*. Ask all the children present on the carpet if this number is more or less than the last one spoken. For example, 49 is less than 56. If it is less they show thumbs down, if it is more they show thumbs up. Keep going like this, asking each child who arrives to say a 2-digit number and then asking all children present to indicate whether this number is more or less than the last number spoken.

Adaptations

Can also be used for:

- 3-digit numbers   (Y2+)

Doubling and halving

FMF2.I5   Double the claps

(YI) Double the numbers to I0

Children sit in a circle as they arrive on the carpet. One child claps, the next child says the number of claps and the third child doubles this number and says the total. Then the next child claps, the one after says the number of claps and the next child doubles this and says the total. Keep going like this, keeping up a fast pace and allowing children to join the circle as they arrive. If a child either counts the number of claps incorrectly or doubles the number incorrectly, they stand up, They get a second chance when it comes round to their turn again.

Adaptations

Can also be used for:

* doubling the numbers up to 5   (F)

Doubling and halving

FMF2.16   Double doubles

(Y2) Double numbers to 20

Children sit in small lines of three, one behind the other. The first child says a number up to 12 and pretends to pass it over their shoulder to the second child. For example, they say *Eleven*. The second child doubles it and pretends to pass the total over their shoulder to the last child. For example, they say *Twenty-two*. The last child says the double of this number, for example *Forty-four*. If they are correct, they stand up and come round to sit at the front of the line. They then say a number up to 12 and play starts again. Which threesome can maintain a fast pace and keep getting all of their doubles correct?

Adaptations

Can also be used for:

- doubling multiples of 5 , for example *35 doubled is 70 and 70 doubled is?*   (Y2+)

Times-tables

FMF2.17   Backwards tables

(Y2) Know the two times-table

Tell children *We are doing backwards tables.* You say the answer to a two times-table fact and they say how many 2s this is using their fingers. Choose a child and say *Fourteen.* They have to quickly count in 2s to 14 using their fingers and say *Seven.* Then all rehearse in unison the fact, *Seven twos are fourteen.* Choose another child and say *Twenty.* They have to count in 2s using their fingers and say *Ten.* Rehearse the fact, *Ten twos are twenty.* Continue like this, saying *Eight* to the next child. If children can say the number without counting along their fingers, that is even better!

Adaptations

Can also be used for:

- five times-table   (Y2)
- ten times-table   (Y2)

Times-tables

FMF2.18   Stop the chant

(Y2) Know the two times-table

Start with five or six children who are ready on the carpet. Start chanting the two times-table, *One two is two, two twos are four, three twos are six*, etc. As a new child arrives, pause. Ask them to say the next line in the chant, for example *Four twos are eight*. If they say this line correctly, the whole group resumes the chant on the next line, for example *Five twos are ten, six twos are twelve*, etc. When the chant eventually ends, start again. Each time a new child arrives, the group stops and that child says the next line on their own. This activity involves keeping track and constantly swapping between the whole group and individual children.

Adaptations

Can also be used for:

- five times-table   (Y2)
- ten times-table   (Y2)

Section 3: Activities for those spare 5 minutes

Advice to teachers

- Keep the pace brisk – the activities rely on a brisk pace and a no-nonsense approach.
- These are action-packed activities, often involving physical movement so that children are not sitting still. Hopefully all of the children will want to join in!
- Make sure each child has a space to stand in, as the activity may require them to jump or hop or wave their arms. However, these activities are intended to be done in the classroom so they do not require a hall or playground.
- Keep the activities really active as well as fast-moving. Do not attempt to tell children off or reprove them. These activities are intended to be fun, not work!
- The key to successful activities is generating a 'can do' atmosphere and giving children a lot of confidence and praise. Keep stressing how good children are getting at knowing their number facts. Keep telling them that they are all really improving at maths now and they will be brilliant mathematicians when they reach the juniors!

Counting

FMF3.I Making 6

(F) Knowing the pairs of numbers that make 6

Ask children to each stand in a space facing you. Say *Bird* and
then say a I-digit number less than 6. Children do the number of
bird wing flaps that add to your number to make 6. For example,
you say *Two* and they do four wing flaps. Reiterate by saying the
addition, *Two and four make six.* Then say *Bunny* and another
I-digit number less than 6. Children do the number of bunny
hops that add to your number to make 6. For example, you say
Three and they do three bunny hops. Reiterate by saying the
addition, *Three and three make six.* Continue, saying a creature
and a number every time. Other creatures you could use include
frog (little jumps), kangaroo (big jumps), fish (swimming arm
movements), squirrel (small digging or climbing movements) or
horse (trotting on the spot).

Adaptations

Can also be used for:

- saying numbers that make the pairs to 7, 8, and 9   (F / YI)
- saying the numbers for the bonds to I0   (YI / Y2)

Counting

FMF3.2   Once upon a time

(F) Counting to I2, recognising quantities

Children sit together on the floor. Say *Once upon a time there were...* and point to a child. They say *One* and go to stand in another part of the classroom. Point to another child who says *Two* and joins the first child. Point to a third child who says *Three* and joins the other two children. Continue like this until seven children are standing together. *Once upon a time there were seven dwarves.* Confirm with children that this is the story of Snow White. Then say *Once upon a time there were...* Point to a child on the floor. They say *One* and go to stand in a different part of the classroom. Point to a second child who says *Two* and joins the first child. Continue until there are twelve children. *Once upon a time there were twelve dancing princesses.* Continue with other counts until all children are in a group, for example three little pigs, three billy goats gruff, two ugly sisters, one little girl called Red Riding Hood. Compare the groups. Which group is the largest? Which group is the smallest?

Adaptations

Can also be used for:

- numbers in nursery rhymes, for example three blind mice   (F)

Counting

FMF3.3   Touch your toes

(F) Saying the next two numbers in a count

Children all stand up. Choose a child and say a number to them. They say the next two numbers. As they say the first number, they bend to touch their toes. As they say the second number, they reach up and raise their hands above their head. For example, you say *Twelve*. The child says *Thirteen* as they touch their toes, and *Fourteen* as they reach up. If they are not able to do this quickly or correctly, they kneel down. Continue going round the class, keeping a fast pace. Sometimes return to children who are kneeling so that they get a second chance.

Adaptations

Can also be used for:

- saying the numbers 1 and 2 less than a given number   (Y1)
- saying the numbers 10 and 20 more than a given number   (Y2)

Counting

FMF3.4   Trains of ten

(YI) Counting in I0s from any given number

Children sit together on the floor. Choose a child and say a number to them. They respond with the number 10 more. For example, you say *Six*, they say *Sixteen*. If they are correct, they start to walk very slowly, heel to toe, across the room. Point to another child who says the number 10 more than that, *Twenty-six*. If they are correct, they quickly join the first child, stand behind them, putting a hand on their shoulder, and walk slowly across the room with them. Point to a third child who says the number 10 more, *Thirty-six*. If they are correct, they join the other two children walking slowly across the room. Any child who cannot say the next number quickly and correctly sits back down. Return to them later to give them a second chance. Continue, maintaining a fast pace. When you cross 100 either carry on, helping with hundreds, or start again with a new number.

Adaptations

Can also be used for:

- saying the number 1 more   (F)
- saying the number 2 more   (YI / Y2)
- saying the number 5 more   (Y2)

Counting

FMF3.5   Hands on hips

(Y1) Counting on 2

Children stand with their hands on their hips. Mime throwing a number to a child. That child takes their hands from their hips and mimes catching the number. As they do this, they say the number 2 less. For example, you say *Seventeen*, the child says *Fifteen*. If the child is correct they put their hands by their sides. If not, they put their hands back on their hips. Continue, keeping a fast pace. Sometimes return to children with their hands by their sides so that they get a second chance.

Adaptations

Can also be used for:

- saying the number 1 more or 1 less   (F / Y1)
- saying the number 10 more or 10 less   (Y1 / Y2)
- saying the number 5 more   (Y2)
- saying the number 9 more   (Y2+)

Counting

FMF3.6   Rhyming twos

(Y2) Counting in 2s

Teach children the *Counting in 2s action rhyme* (Appendix 2). Start by chanting it yourself and asking children to copy the actions. Repeat the rhyme over and over and encourage children to join in with the words once they know them. Each time you reach the last line of the rhyme, remind children to shout it. Once children are familiar with the rhyme, pause on a number and ask children how many 2s make this number. For example, pause after twelve, and ask *How many twos in twelve?* Children reply with the answer, *Six.* Return to the rhyme and continue chanting, pausing every so often to ask another question.

Adaptations

Can also be used for:

- asking children to make up their own lines for each number in the 2s count   (Y2)

Counting

FMF3.7   Threes in action

(Y2) Counting in 3s

Teach children the *Counting in 3s action rhyme* (Appendix 3).
Start by chanting it yourself and asking children to copy the
actions. Repeat the rhyme over and over and encourage children
to join in with the words once they know them. Each time you
reach the last line of the rhyme, remind children to shout it. Once
children are familiar with the rhyme, ask them to make up some
lines of their own that rhyme with the 3s count.

Adaptations

Can also be used for:

- asking children to make up a rhyme for the 5s count   (Y2)

Addition

FMF3.8   Hands on heads

(F / Y1) Making teen numbers as 10 and some 1s

Ask every child to stand with their hands on their head. Choose a child, say a 1-digit number and mime throwing it to them. They take their hands from their head, mime catching the number and say the number plus 10. For example, you throw *Seven* and they say *Seventeen*. Continue with other children, keeping a fast pace. If a child is not able to answer quickly or correctly then they put their hands back on their head.

Adaptations

Can also be used for:

- adding 10 to a 2-digit number, for example 24 + 10   (Y1)
- adding a multiple of ten, for example 20 or 30   (Y2)

Addition

FMF3.9 Finger bingo

(Y2) Adding to the next multiple of ten

Children sit down at their tables, hold both hands in the air and show any number of fingers, for example three fingers. Children look around and try to make sure that their number is different from their nearest neighbours'. Say a 2-digit number that is not a multiple of ten. If children are showing the number of fingers that add to your number to make the next multiple of ten then they stand up. For example, if you say *Forty-seven*, children showing three fingers stand up. Repeat, with children holding up a different number of fingers and you saying another 2-digit number. If a child is correct and already standing, then they stay standing. Continue until you have rehearsed several bonds to 10, and as many of the class as possible are standing.

Adaptations

Can also be used for:

- making the bonds to 10   (Y1 / Y2)
- making the bonds to 20   (Y2)
- making the bonds to any number up to 20   (Y2+)

Addition

FMF3.10   Back to back

(Y2) Adding amounts to make one pound

Children stand in pairs, facing their partner. Choose a pair. Say a number of coins, for example *Three 20ps*. Mostly use 10ps, 20ps and 50ps, but include 5ps for pairs who are more able. The pair agrees together how much more you need to make a pound and tells you the answer, for example *40p*. If they answer quickly and correctly, they stay facing each other. If they are slow or incorrect, they turn and stand back to back. Repeat, choosing another pair, and say a different number of coins. Sometimes return to children who are standing back to back so that they get a second chance.

Adaptations

Can also be used for:

- saying pairs of numbers that make the numbers 11–20   (Y2)
- saying pairs of numbers that add to 60   (Y2)

Number bonds

FMF3.II   Rhyming bonds

(YI / Y2) Knowing the number bonds to I0

Children sit in pairs. Say a line from *Rhyming number bonds* (Appendix 5), for example *We're in a fix*. Pairs who recognise the bond to I0 that it rhymes with quickly show the bond on their fingers, with one child showing the first number and the other child showing the second number. For example, four and six rhymes with *We're in a fix* so one child shows four fingers and the other shows six fingers. Use a lot of different short sayings for children to practise this. For example, *Flat on the floor* (6 + 4), *Bees in a hive* (5 + 5), *Chocolate heaven* (3 + 7), *Shut the gate* (2 + 8), *My team won* (9 + 1). Reward pairs who are the quickest to show the correct bond.

Adaptations

Can also be used for:

- saying pairs of numbers that make the numbers II–20 (ask children to invent the rhymes)   (Y2)

Number bonds

FMF3.12   Ready, steady, go. Show me!

(Y2) Knowing the number bonds to 20

Children sit in pairs with their legs outstretched. Say *Ready, steady, go. Show me!* Each pair discusses how they will use their hands and feet to show a bond to 20, then gets into position. Children stretch their legs out to represent a ten, or draw their legs in to represent no tens. This means that in each pair, only one child should have their legs outstretched. For example, one child has their legs outstretched and holds up three fingers to show thirteen. Their partner draws their legs in and holds up seven fingers to show seven. Ask different pairs to say their bond, for example *Thirteen and seven*. Repeat several times, making sure that you ask pairs to say a different bond to 20 each time.

Adaptations

Can also be used for:

- saying pairs of numbers that make the numbers 6, 7, 8 or 9   (F)
- saying pairs of numbers that make 10   (Y1)

Number bonds

FMF3.13   Whisper the sum

(Y2) Number bonds of numbers between 10 and 20

Children sit in pairs. Each pair chooses a number between 10 and 20, then sits quietly. When every pair has chosen, say a number. Each pair whispers to each other the number that goes with your number to make their number. For example, a pair has chosen 15. You say *Six*, they whisper *Nine* to each other. Choose several pairs to say their additions aloud, for example *Six and nine make fifteen*. Repeat several times, rewarding pairs who are correct.

Adaptations

Can also be used for:

- saying pairs of numbers that make any number up to 10   (Y1)
- saying pairs of multiples of ten that add to 100   (Y2)

Subtraction

FMF3.14   Fast fingers

(F / Y1) Subtracting 10 from teen numbers

Children stand with their hands behind their backs. Say a number, then say *Ready, steady, go!* Children take 10 away from your number and show you that many fingers. For example, you say *Fifteen*, children show you five fingers. Children who do this correctly sit down and continue playing. Children who are sitting and show the correct number of fingers next time stand up again. Continue, keeping a fast pace.

Adaptations

Can also be used for:

- doubling the numbers to 5   (F / Y1)
- halving the even numbers to 20   (Y1 / Y2)

More or less

FMF3.15   Whisper whisper

(Y1) Say numbers 1 more and 1 less

Sit with children in a circle. Identify the child opposite you in the circle and ask them to stand or kneel. Explain that you will whisper a number to the child next to you and then they will whisper the number 1 more to their neighbour, who will then whisper the number 1 more to their neighbour and so on. You whisper a number to the child on your left, and they whisper the number 1 more to the child on their left and so on. You also whisper a number to the child on your right, and they whisper the number 1 more to the child on their right and so on, round the circle. Eventually the child standing up will receive two numbers whispered to them. They have to say them both. Children must decide which number is smaller and which is larger. Check that these two numbers are both correct. Repeat this activity, asking children to whisper the number 1 less.

Adaptations

Can also be used for:

- saying 10 more or 10 less instead of 1 more or less   (Y2)

More or less

FMF3.16   Which way round?

(Y2) Recognise numbers which are less and more

Put children in pairs. Explain that one child will be the 10s and show fingers to match the 10s in a number, and the other will be the 1s and will show fingers to match the 1s in a number. Get children to decide who will show 10s and who will show 1s in their pair. Say a number, for example, *Thirty-five*. Ask children to show this on their fingers. The 10s child shows three fingers and the 1s child shows five fingers. Everyone shows you 35 like this. Stress three 10s and five 1s. If possible, write this on the board, 35. Then say the number the other way round, for example, *Fifty-three*. Ask children to show this in the same way, the 10s child showing five fingers and the 1s child showing three fingers. If possible, write this on the board, 53. Ask each pair to decide which number is smaller and which is larger. Remind them that the number where the 10s child shows more fingers is the larger number. Repeat this, saying different numbers each time.

Adaptations

Can also be used for:

- 3-digit numbers   (Y2+)

Doubling and halving

FMF3.17   Head, shoulders, knees and toes

(Y1 / Y2) Doubling numbers to 12

Children stand with their hands on their heads. Say a number between 1 and 13. Children quickly say the double together. Those who are correct move their hands to their shoulders. Those who are incorrect keep their hands on their head. Say another number. Again children quickly say the double. Those who are correct move their hands from their shoulders to their knees or from their head to their shoulders if they were incorrect the first time. Say another number. Once again, children quickly say the double and if correct, move their hands on one place, for example from their knees to their toes. Say another number. Children who are correct move their hands on one place. Those who had their hands on their toes last time now stand up straight with their hands by their sides. *Who managed to get all the way through head, shoulders, knees and toes?*

Adaptations

Can also be used for:

- doubling the numbers to 6   (F / Y1)
- halving the even numbers to 24   (Y1 / Y2)

Doubling and halving

FMF3.18   Curl up, stand up

(Y2) Doubling numbers to 20

Say a number. Each child decides whether to double or halve it.
If they double it, they stand up. If they halve it, they curl up their
legs and hold them in their arms. Choose all the children who are
curled up. They are going to say the number that is half of your
number. Say your number and they say half of it in unison. Watch
to see who does not know this. If they are correct, they may
uncurl their legs. Then choose all the children standing up and
ask them to say the double of your number. Repeat your number
and they say the double in unison. Watch to see who does not
know this. If they are correct, they sit down. Repeat this activity,
saying another starting number and allowing children to decide
whether to double or halve it. Include some odd numbers.

Adaptations

Can also be used for:

* doubling and halving multiples of ten up to 60   (Y2)

Times-tables

FMF3.19 Rhyming tables

(Y2) Knowing the two times-table

Point to a child. Ask them to say the first line of the two times-table and also to say the rhyming line from the *Two times-table action rhyme* (Appendix 4). *One two is two, what can you do?* Repeat with the whole class, doing the actions together. Then point to another child. They say the second line of the two times-table, as well as the rhyming line. Repeat the first two lines with the whole class, doing the actions together. Point to a child who says the third line then repeat all three lines with the whole class, doing the actions together. Continue until you have completed the whole rhyme.

Adaptations

Can also be used for:

- inventing their own action rhyme for the three times-table   (Y2+)

Times-tables

FMF3.20   Chanting with the twos

(Y2) Chant in 2s from two

Point to four or five children. Ask them to chant the 2s in unison, *Two, four, six...* When you get to *Eight*, pause and the whole class joins in with *Who do we appreciate?* Continue, choosing four or five different children to chant together *Ten, twelve, fourteen, sixteen*, then the whole class joins in with *What are they making in the kitchen?* Continue like this, choosing another four or five children to say the next four numbers in the chant. At 24 the whole class can say, *If it's good we'll eat some more!* Repeat this from the beginning, starting again with four or five different children.

Adaptations

Can also be used for:

- five times-table: *Five, ten, fifteen, twenty*, then pause for the whole class to say, *Yummy, yummy, I eat plenty!* Then *Twenty-five, thirty, thirty-five, forty*, and pause for the whole class to say, *Spilling dinner is a bit naughty!* Then *Forty-five, fifty, fifty-five, sixty* and whole class says *Naughty wizards are a bit tricksy!*   (Y2)
- ten times-table: *Ten, twenty, thirty, forty*, and pause for the whole class to say *Cheeky Charlie is a bit naughty! Fifty, sixty, seventy, eighty, Cheeky Charlie is a bit flakey! Ninety, one hundred! Charlie thundered!*   (Y2)

Times-tables

FMF3.2I On pause!

(Y2) Say how many 2s in a multiple of two

Chant the multiples of two. At a certain point in the chant, tap a child on the shoulders very gently. The chant stops and the child who was selected has to say how many 2s are in that multiple. For example, the chant goes *Two, four, six, eight...* and then you tap a child on the shoulders. The child says the number of 2s in 8, *Four*. If they do not know the answer, tap another child. Once the correct answer has been said, resume the chant. Tap another child. They have to say how many 2s are in the number reached when you tap. Keep going like this. When the chant reaches 24, start again at 2. Keep practising this activity. Even children who know their tables will find it difficult.

Adaptations

Can also be used for:
- five times-table   (Y2)
- ten times-table   (Y2)

Appendix

I. A ship came from China

A ship came from China with a cargo of tea,

All laden with presents for you and for me.

It brought me a _____ *(Fill in with a number or a shape as appropriate)*

Just imagine my bliss,

When I played with my _____ like this, like this.

(Child waves a matching number of fingers or draws the shape in the air, as appropriate)

2. Counting in 2s action rhyme

Two, four, six, eight,

Who do we appreciate?   (Hold hands out, palms up, shrug shoulders)

Ten, twelve and fourteen,

We're so fast we can't be seen.   (Run on the spot)

Sixteen, eighteen, twenty, so...

Now you see how fast we go!   (Run on the spot)

Twenty-two and twenty-four,

Tables ended. Close the door!   (Shout this last line and clap hands loudly)

3. Counting in 3s action rhyme

Three, six, nine,

Tell me the time.   (Look at a watch)

Twelve, fifteen, eighteen,

Don't you keep me waiting.   (Waggle a finger)

Twenty-one and twenty-four,

Someone's knocking at the door.   (Knock at a door)

Twenty-seven, thirty, Grin...   (Grin)

Now we'd better let them in.   (Beckon)

Thirty-three and thirty-six,

Now it's time for tea and bics.   (Shout this last line)

4. Two times-table action rhyme

One two is two, what can you do? (Hold hands out, palms up, shrug shoulders)

Two twos are four, knock at the door. (Make knocking action with clenched hand)

Three twos are six, oh what a fix! (Waggle finger as if telling someone off)

Four twos are eight, please open the gate. (Make gate opening gesture)

Five twos are ten, now shut it again. (Make gate shutting gesture)

Six twos are twelve, books on the shelves. (Reach up to put book on top shelf)

Seven twos are fourteen, where have you been? (Waggle finger as if telling someone off)

Eight twos are sixteen, who have you seen? (Put hand above eyes and peer into distance)

Nine twos are eighteen, perhaps it's the queen? (Put a crown on your own head)

Ten twos are twenty, there's food a-plenty. (Eating with a spoon)

Eleven twos are twenty-two, all the more for me and you. (Eating with a spoon)

Twelve twos are twenty-four, now you've finished sit on the floor. (Sit down on the floor)

5. Rhyming number bonds

6 + 4	Knock at the door; Lions can roar; ...
4 + 6	We're in a fix; Pick up sticks; ...
5 + 5	Bees in a hive; Duck and dive; ...
3 + 7	Chocolate heaven; Holidays in Devon; ...
7 + 3	Busy bee; Birds in a tree; ...
2 + 8	Shut the gate; Peas on a plate; ...
8 + 2	Sky is blue; Cows say moo; ...
1 + 9	Weather is fine; Fishing line; ...
9 + 1	Hot cross bun; Having fun; ...
10 + 0	You're my hero; Emperor Nero...

Author
Ruth Merttens

Published by Pearson Education Limited, Edinburgh Gate, Harlow, Essex, CM20 2JE.

www.pearsonschools.co.uk

Text © Pearson Education Limited 2012

Typeset by Tracey Camden
Cover design by Pearson Education Limited
Printed in the UK by Ashford Colour Press Ltd.

The author asserts their moral right to be identified as the author of this work

First published 2012

16 15 14 13 12
10 9 8 7 6 5 4 3 2 1

British Library Cataloguing in Publication Data
A catalogue record for this book is available from the British Library

ISBN 978 1 447 92592 7

Acknowledgements
Every effort has been made to contact copyright holders of material reproduced in this book. Any omissions will be rectified in subsequent printings if notice is given to the publishers.